A TO Z
QUIZZES

First published in 2002 by Miles Kelly Publishing Ltd,
Bardfield Centre, Great Bardfield, Essex, CM7 4SL

Copyright © Miles Kelly Publishing Ltd 2002

This edition printed 2002

ISBN 1-84236-129-5

2 4 6 8 10 9 7 5 3

Project Manager: Ian Paulyn
Assistant: Lisa Clayden
Design: Clare Sleven

Contact us by email: info@mileskelly.net
Website: www.mileskelly.net

Printed in India

A TO Z QUIZZES

by
Christopher Rigby

Miles Kelly
PUBLISHING

About the Author

Born in Blackburn, Lancashire in 1960, Christopher Rigby has been compiling and presenting pub quizzes for the past 15 years. When he is not adding to his material for quizzes, Christopher works in the car industry. He is married to Clare – they have two teenage daughters, Hollie and Ashley and share their home with two demented dogs called Vespa and Bailey. A keen Manchester United fan Christopher lists his heroes as George Best and Homer Simpson.

A to Z QUIZZES EXPLAINED

The following book comprises 45 A to Z quizzes. Each quiz has 26 questions. The answers correspond to the appropriate letter of the alphabet. For example;

 A Canberra is the capital city of which country? (Australia)
 B In Eastenders who plays Peggy Butcher?
   (Barbara Windsor)
 C What is a young elephant called? (Calf)

QUIZ ONE

A Which town is closely associated with the patron saint of animals, St Francis?

B What was Jackie Kennedy's maiden name?

C What name is given to the French-speaking inhabitants of Louisiana?

D What is the American word for a nappy?

E What word describes the focal point of an earthquake?

F What name is given to the force that opposes motion and produces heat?

G What is the name of Pinocchio's father?

H Which musical instrument was Larry Adler famous for playing?

I What word describes a narrow strip of land joining two larger land masses?

J From what sort of berries is gin distilled?

K Which visual toy was invented by David Brewster?

L What is the capital city of Zambia?

M What name is given to an engine-powered hang glider?

ANSWERS

A. Assisi B. Bouvier C. Cajuns D. Diaper E. Epicentre F. Friction G. Gepetto H. Harmonica I. Isthmus J. Juniper K. Kaleidoscope L. Lusaka M. Microlite

QUIZ ONE

N What is the capital city of Cyprus?

O What is the opposite of the word 'transparent'?

P Which 'ology' is the study of bumps on the head?

Q What was the first drug ever used to treat malaria?

R Which Dutch pop group topped the charts in 1994 with the song 'Cotton-Eyed Joe'?

S What name is given to the home of a badger?

T What did the country of Formosa change its name to?

U Name the actress who played the daughter of Alf Garnett.

V Who is the Roman goddess of the hearth?

W In which club was Arthur Daley served his vodka & tonics by Dave?

X Which five-letter prefix is used to denote the colour yellow?

Y Who became the leader of the PLO in 1969?

Z What is the main currency unit of Poland?

ANSWERS

N. Nicosia O. Opaque P. Phrenology Q. Quinine R. Rednex S. Sett T. Taiwan U. Una Stubbs V. Vesta W. Winchester X. Xanth Y. Yasser Arafat Z. Zloty

QUIZ TWO

A What is the first day of Lent called?

B Who is the Roman god of wine?

C What is the largest lake in the world?

D What name is given to a camel with one hump?

E What is the name of the largest species of antelope?

F What is the medical name for the longest bone in the human body?

G Which is the second largest Channel Island?

H Which is the second largest of America's Great Lakes?

I Which eight-letter word is the name given to foot soldiers?

J Who won the World Snooker Championships in 1998?

K What is the name of Superman's home planet?

L What name is given to aching in the lower back?

M What is the technical term for the speed of sound?

ANSWERS
A. Ash Wednesday B. Bacchus C. Caspian Sea D. Dromedary E. Eland F. Femur
G. Guernsey H. Huron I. Infantry J. John Higgins K. Krypton L. Lumbago M. Mach I

8

QUIZ TWO

N What name is given to the control centre of a cell?

O Who was Shakespeare's King of the Fairies?

P What was the surname of the singer who was nicknamed 'The Little Sparrow'?

Q What is a quarter of a circle called?

R What is the vibrating piece of a woodwind instrument known as?

S What would be of particular interest to a conchologist?

T What was the name of the small robotic buddy of Buck Rogers?

U Which No. 1 hit for Billy Joel was written for Christine Brinkley?

V What name is given to an air-free space?

W What sort of bird featured on a farthing?

X What name is given to a morbid fear of foreigners?

Y Which song was a No. 1 hit in 1970 for the group Christie?

Z What was invented by Whitcomb Judson?

ANSWERS

N. Nucleus O. Oberon P. Piaf Q. Quadrant R. Reed S. Shells T. Tweekie U. Uptown Girl V. Vacuum W. Wren X. Xenophobia Y. 'Yellow River' Z. Zip

9

QUIZ THREE

A Who was the first ever woman to fly solo across the Atlantic Ocean?

B What sort of shops were legalised in Britain in May 1961?

C What name is given to the scarlet dye obtained from beetles?

D Which word of German origin is the name given to a ghostly replica of a living person?

E Which Ugandan airport was the scene of a hostage incident in 1975?

F What is the alternative name for a hazelnut?

G What does an auctioneer bang to close a sale?

H What is signified by the number 12 on the Beaufort scale?

I What legal word is used to describe the situation of a person who has died without leaving a will?

J What did Luke Skywalker finally become in the final *Star Wars* film?

K What provides the staple diet of the blue whale?

L What name is given to a person who compiles dictionaries?

M Who was the man who provided the music for the Wombles?

ANSWERS

A. Amelia Earhart B. Betting Shops C. Cochineal D. Doppelganger E. Entebbe F. Filbert G. Gavel H. Hurricane I. Intestate J. Jedi Knight K. Krill L. Lexicographer M. Mike Batt

QUIZ THREE

N What six-letter word is the name of the petrol-thickening jelly that is used in the manufacturing of bombs?

O What sort of branch is a symbol of peace?

P What do we get from a combination of lead and tin?

Q What name is given to a sub-atomic particle and is also a type of soft cheese?

R What is the alternative name for the tree known as the mountain ash?

S What is the literal English translation of the word Islam?

T What clothes pattern was it against the law to wear in England in 1746?

U What is the name of the famous art gallery in Florence?

V What is the name given to the science of grape-growing?

W What is the non-technical term for a keratosis of the skin?

X What was invented by the German physicist Roentgen?

Y Describe the garment worn by the leader of the Tour de France.

Z What surname was Bob Dylan born with?

ANSWERS

N. Napalm O. Olive branch P. Pewter Q. Quark R. Rowan S. Submission T. Tartan U. Uffizi V. Viticulture W. Wart X. X rays Y. Yellow Jersey Z. Zimmerman

QUIZ FOUR

A What is the name of the largest artery in the human body?

B What name is given to the study of projectiles?

C Who shouted for order at the Wheeltappers & Shunters Club?

D What name is given to the light winds that blow across the Equator?

E What was the name of the lioness that featured in the film *Born Free*?

F What is the name of Rossini's Barber of Seville?

G What name was given to Abraham Lincoln's famous speech of 1863?

H What is the chemical symbol for mercury?

I What is the alternative title of the 'Shoop, Shoop Song'?

J Who was the Poet Laureate from 1972 to 1984?

K In which combat sport would a competitor use a bamboo sword?

L What do limnologists study?

M How is marsh gas otherwise know?

QUIZ FOUR

N Who is the only Englishman to be appointed Pope?

O Which empire succeeded the Seljuk Empire?

P What is the name of Britain's smallest species of bat?

Q Which five-letter word is the name given to a short-handled riding whip?

R Who overslept for twenty years in the Catskill Mountains?

S What name is given to the marks that resemble the crucifixion wounds of Jesus?

T Which part of an insect's body connects its head to its abdomen?

U What name is given to the shadow of the Earth on the moon?

V What was the American equivalent of the British music hall?

W What is the more common name for the trachea?

X Which four-letter prefix is used to signify the word wood?

Y The Shakespeare character Hamlet said 'I knew him so well'. Who was he referring to?

Z What was the name of the port associated with the *Herald of Free Enterprise* car ferry that sank in 1987?

QUIZ FIVE

A Whose girlfriend was called Looby Lou?

B Which 1960s western series featured the Cartwright family?

C Which game show features a computer called Mr Chips?

D Who did Richard Chamberlain portray when he worked at Blair General Hospital?

E Which long-running TV series is set in the town of Beckindale?

F At which hotel was Major Gowen a resident guest?

G What was the name of the school created by Phil Redmond?

H Which children's TV series featured the characters Zsa Zsa the cat and Miss Kiki Frog?

I Sergeant Lewis is the sidekick of which TV police detective?

J What was the title of the comedy drama that told of the stormy relationship of Vince and Penny?

K In which American TV series did George Savalas play Stavros?

L Grace Van Owen and Arnold Becker were leading characters in which TV show?

M What was Patrick Duffy known as when he had webbed fingers and toes?

QUIZ FIVE

N What is the title of the award-winning drama series which stars Dennis Franz as Andy Sipowitz?

O Which sitcom features the Trotter family?

P Which TV drama is set at the Wentworth Detention Centre?

Q Which sci-fi series featured Dr Samuel Beckett travelling through time?

R In which ITN drama does the lead character refer to his wife as 'she who must be obeyed'?

S In the opening credits of which comedy series did we hear the words 'These are the Tates and there are the Campbells'?

T Which cartoon character was continually at loggerheads with Officer Dibble?

U In which comedy series did Frankie Howard find himself in Ancient Rome?

V Which Dutch detective was played by Barry Foster?

W In which cartoon series did Penelope Pitstop drive the Compact Pussycat?

X Which TV series would you associate with the phrase 'The truth is out there'?

Y How are Neil, Mike, Vivian and Rik collectively known?

Z Which 1960s cop show was set in Newtown?

ANSWERS

N. NYPD Blue O. Only Fools and Horses P. Prisoner Cell Block H Q. Quantum Leap R. Rumpole of the Bailey S. Soap T. Top Cat U. Up Pompeii! V. Van Der Valk W. Wacky Races X. X Files Y. Young Ones Z. Z Cars

QUIZ ONE

....

A What name is given to the golden halo that appears around the head of a saint?

B What four-letter word is the name given to a vertical wall of water?

C What name is given to the science of the study of time?

D What is a male duck called?

E What is the hardest substance in the human body?

F What is a blacksmith's workshop called?

G Which novel by Damon Runyon became a musical film starring Marlon Brando?

H What is the collective term for any plant-eating animal?

I What is generally regarded as the tallest breed of dog?

J What name is given to the dinosaur period of time?

K On which Greek island could you visit the castle ruins of Hippocrates?

L What is the seventh sign of the zodiac?

M What is the American equivalent of an undertaker?

QUIZ ONE

N On TV who has played a Liver bird and a district nurse?

O What word describes a four-sided stone shaft, topped with a pyramid?

P What name is given to the principal female singer in an opera?

Q What name is given to the thrower in American Football?

R What is the last book of the Bible?

S Which sport is a Scottish version of hockey?

T What name is given to the study of religious doctrine?

U Osiris is the Egyptian god of the what?

V Where do Watford FC play their home matches?

W What name is given to the ridge on the shoulders of a horse?

X Which Chinese city is home to the Terracotta Army?

Y What name is given to a Tibetan ox?

Z Which ski resort is located at the foot of the Matterhorn?

ANSWERS
N. Nerys Hughes O. Obelisk P. Prima donna Q. Quarterback R. Book of Revelations
S. Shinty T. Theology U. Underworld V. Vicarage Road W. Withers X. Xian Y. Yak
Z. Zermatt

QUIZ TWO

A In the Church of England what rank comes below a bishop?

B In the Army what rank is directly above a colonel?

C What is the largest species of vulture?

D What is the collective term for a group of pigs?

E What is the name of the legendary South American city of gold?

F Which fencing sword is used by female competitors?

G What word would describe a dozen dozen?

H What is the name of *The Sun* newspaper's comic-strip Viking?

I Which American state is nicknamed the Gem State?

J What is the name of the main vein in the neck?

K What name is given to the inner tower of a castle?

L Which Irish town would you associate with a humorous five-lined poem?

M Who is the patron saint of soldiers?

ANSWERS

A. Archdeacon B. Brigadier C. Condor D. Drove E. El Dorado F. Foil G. Gross H. Hagar the Horrible I. Idaho J. Jugular K. Keep L. Limerick M. Michael

QUIZ TWO

N In the Bible who was the father of Shem, Ham and Japheth?

O Which Dickens novel features a villain called Silas Wegg?

P What name is given to the liquid part of the blood?

Q Which TV coroner was portrayed by Jack Klugman?

R What name was adopted by the followers of Oliver Cromwell?

S Which bone of the ear shares its name with a jockey's foot supports?

T What is the alternative name for a white ant?

U Who did Jackie Coogan play in *The Addams Family*?

V By what name are the chambers of the heart know?

W What is a common name for a lycanthrope?

X What technical name is given to a rock that is found in a system to which it does not belong?

Y What was the title of the song that provided Michael Jackson with a UK No. 1 hit in 1995?

Z What name is given to the study of animals?

ANSWERS

N. Noah O. *Our Mutual Friend* P. Plasma Q. Quincy R. Roundheads S. Stirrup T. Termite U. Uncle Fester V. Ventricles W. Werewolf X. Xenolith Y. 'You Are Not Alone' Z. Zoology

QUIZ THREE

A Which musical instrument was invented in Berlin in 1822?

B What name is given to the study of plants?

C In the Roman Catholic Church what name is given to the cup containing the Mass wine?

D Which airport serves the city of Aberdeen?

E What race of people have a name that literally means 'eater of raw flesh'?

F What kind of headgear favoured by Tommy Cooper was named after a Moroccan town?

G What is the birthstone for January?

H In the Bible who was the stepfather of Salome?

I In which sitcom did Larry Hagman play the character of Tony Nelson?

J What was the name of Captain Hook's ship in *Peter Pan*?

K What animal has a name that literally means 'no drink'?

L What name is given to a picture made from a drawing on a stone?

M Which breed of cat would you associate with the Isle of Man?

ANSWERS

A. Accordion B. Botany C. Chalice D. Dyce E. Eskimo F. Fez G. Garnet H. Herod I. I *Dream of Jeannie* J. *Jolly Roger* K. Koala Bear L. Lithograph M. Manx

QUIZ THREE

N On TV who played the Charmer?

O What name is given to a sacred story that has been set to music?

P On TV who was the boss of Della Street?

Q In which film did Peter Ustinov play Emperor Nero?

R Who painted 'The Night Watch'?

S What is the seventh largest island in the world?

T What name is given to an appliance that regulates pressure and temperature?

U Feargal Sharkey was the lead singer of which punk band?

V What name describes the process for hardening rubber?

W What were mistook for monsters by Don Quixote?

X Which gas was discovered in 1898?

Y What is the main currency of Japan?

Z What was the surname of the man who invented the airship?

ANSWERS

N. Nigel Havers O. Oratorio P. Perry Mason Q. *Quo Vadis* R. Rembrandt S. Sumatra T. Thermostat U. Undertones V. Vulcanisation W. Windmills X. Xenon Y. Yen Z. Zeppelin

QUIZ FOUR

A In which city would you visit the Taj Mahal?

B What name is given to an open-air night-time entertainment for soldiers?

C Which unit of measurement is equivalent to one tenth of a sea mile?

D Which section of equestrianism is concerned with obedience?

E Who acquired the nickname of the First Lady of Jazz?

F What name is given to a workshop for casting metal?

G Which island is the most southerly of the Windward Islands?

H Which of Shakespeare's plays was set in Agincourt?

I What was the name of the Red Indian tribe led by Hiawatha?

J Which African city was founded in 1886?

K What name is given to the centre of a nut?

L Which five-letter word is the name given to a doctor's deputy?

M What name is given to volcanic molten rock?

QUIZ FOUR

N What name is given to a cloud that is produced by a cluster of stars?

O Which drug is obtained from the poppy?

P What is the collective name given to the colours of red, yellow and blue?

Q What is the smallest member of the partridge family?

R Which famous novel was based on the life of Alexander Selkirk?

S Who became the Men's Wimbledon Singles Champion in 1990?

T What is the name of the principal male hormone in the human body?

U What is the name of the range of mountains located in Central Asia?

V Who composed *The Four Seasons*?

W What is the largest member of the weasel family?

X What word describes an object shaped like a sword?

Y What is the official name for the Tower of London guards?

Z What is the four-letter name of a humped Indian ox?

ANSWERS

N. Nebula O. Opium P. Primary colours Q. Quail R. *Robinson Crusoe* S. Stefan Edberg T. Testosterone U. Urals V. Vivaldi W. Wolverine X. Xiphoid Y. Yeomen of the Guard Z. Zebu

QUIZ FIVE

Name the groups from their hits and the year they were recorded.

A 1987 – 'The Living Daylights'

B 1989 – 'Ride On Time'

C 1972 – 'Sweet Talking Guy'

D 1980 – 'Geno'

E 1968 – 'Baby Come Back'

F 1989 – 'She Drives Me Crazy'

G 1963 – 'I Like It'

H 1983 – 'Temptation'

I 1988 – 'I Need You Tonight'

J 1991 – 'Sit Down'

K 1983 – 'Too Shy'

L 1980 – 'Dance Yourself Dizzy'

M 1977 – 'Chanson D'Amour'

QUIZ FIVE

N 1990 - 'Hangin Tough'

O 1973 - 'Love Train'

P 1987 - 'The Irish Rover'

Q 1977 - 'We Are The Champions'

R 1993 - 'Everybody Hurts'

S 1964 - 'Needles And Pins'

T 1976 - 'Heaven Must Be Missing An Angel'

U 1965 - 'Concrete And Clay'

V 1979 - 'In The Navy'

W 1983 - 'Club Tropicana'

X 1978 - 'Germ Free Adolescents'

Y 1983 - 'Nobody's Diary'

Z 1964 - 'She's Not There'

QUIZ ONE

A Which unit of measurement is equivalent to 4,840 sq yards?

B What is the name of the chief bay on the coast of Bangladesh?

C What does the letter C stand for in the acronym SCUBA?

D Which English county is famed for its clotted cream?

E What was the name of Captain Cook's flagship?

F What is the home of a hare called?

G What is the present-day name for a camelopard?

H What does an endocrinologist study?

I Who wrote the novel *Chitty, Chitty, Bang, Bang*?

J What name is given to the science or philosophy of law?

K In Japan what would be fastened by an obi?

L Which British cathedral has three spires?

M Name the actor who played the title role in the TV drama *Taggart*.

ANSWERS

A. Acre B. Bengal C. Contained D. Devon E. *Endeavour* F. Form G. Giraffe H. Hormones I. Ian Fleming J. Jurisprudence K. Kimono L. Lichfield M. Mark McManus

QUIZ ONE

N Which eight-letter word means the favouring of relatives or friends?

O If the Orient means the East what word means the West?

P Which bird member of the grouse family turns white in the winter?

Q Which muscles are located in the thigh?

R Who played Freddy Kruger on film?

S What name is given to the ova of frogs?

T Which city played host to the 1964 Summer Olympics?

U Which five-letter word means pertaining to the town?

V What is the capital city of Hong Kong?

W Which of Britain's major zoos is located in the county of Bedfordshire?

X Which eight-letter word is defined as a kind of celluloid?

Y From which tree were bows originally made?

Z What was the name of the villain played by Terence Stamp in two Superman films?

3

QUIZ TWO

A Which famous prison was closed in 1963?

B What name is given to the broadest part of a ship's bottom?

C Which cruel activity was banned in Britain in 1849?

D In which book of the Bible did Moses die?

E What was the name of René's wife in the sitcom *Allo, Allo*?

F What is the national cheese of Greece?

G Who was the wife of King Arthur?

H In Britain what was withdrawn from circulation on
   1st January 1970?

I Who built the Clifton Suspension Bridge?

J In a house what name is given to a beam that supports
   the floorboards?

K What was the capital of Pakistan before Islamabad?

L What is the name of the festival that is celebrated on 1st August?

M Which horse won the Grand National in 1990?

ANSWERS

A. Alcatraz B. Bilge C. Cockfighting D. Deuteronomy E. Edith F. Feta G. Guinevere
H. Half crown I. Isambard Kingdom Brunel J. Joist K. Karachi L. Lammas M. Mr Frisk

QUIZ TWO

N Which fruit is a combination of a plum and a peach?

O In a newspaper which column announces deaths?

P What name is given to the science of the study of drugs?

Q Which eight-letter word describes marshy, boggy ground?

R Which children's favourite was created by Mary Tourtel?

S Caviar is obtained from the roe of which fish?

T According to the nursery rhyme, which day's child is full of grace?

U What is the name of the second largest lake in England?

V What is the French word for twenty?

W What beastly nickname was acquired by golfer Craig Stadler?

X What was the name of the horse ridden by the Greek hero Achilles?

Y Which song was a No. I hit for the Bluebells in 1993?

Z What did the Belgian Congo change its name to?

ANSWERS
N. Nectarine O. Obituaries P. Pharmacology Q. Quagmire R. Rupert the Bear S. Sturgeon T. Tuesday U. Ullswater V. Vingt W. Walrus X. Xanthus Y. 'Young at Heart' Z. Zaire

QUIZ THREE

A What is the name of the national airline of Russia?

B Which species of ape is prevalent on the Rock of Gibraltar?

C What name is given to the patterns made by stars?

D What form of headgear was favoured by Sherlock Holmes?

E What is the outer layer of the skin called?

F Which unit of measurement is equivalent to one eighth of a mile?

G Name the process in which steel is covered in zinc.

H Which is the only bird that can fly backwards?

I Which element is obtained from seaweed?

J Which style of music is characterised by syncopated rhythms?

K What name is given to the backbone of a ship?

L What name is given to the beam above a door?

M What is a Muslin place of worship called?

QUIZ THREE

N What type of cloud signifies bad weather?

O What name is given to a unit of electrical resistance?

P Which girl's name is Latin for 'foreseeing'?

Q What is a container for holding arrows called?

R What is measured in curies?

S What was the first commodity to be rationed in World War I?

T What is the name of the large wooded valley located in central Scotland?

U Which company made England's 1998 World Cup strip?

V What was the name of the first spacecraft to land on Mars?

W In the Peanuts cartoon strip what is the name of Snoopy's feathered friend?

X What was issued for a film for the first time in 1950?

Y What is the more common name for lactobacillus bulgaricus?

Z What name is given to the chemistry of fermentation in brewing?

ANSWERS

N. Nimbus O. Ohm P. Prudence Q. Quiver R. Radioactivity S. Sugar T. Trossachs U. Umbro V. Viking W. Woodstock X. Certificate Y. Yoghurt Z. Zymurgy

QUIZ FOUR

A What name is given to a positive electrode?

B Which No. I hit for Art Garfunkel featured in the film *Watership Down*?

C Which infection is known as 'pink eye'?

D What is the alternative name for a cranefly?

E What is a young eel called?

F What was the registration plate of Lady Penelope's pink Rolls Royce?

G In which town was Margaret Thatcher born?

H What name is given to the condition of abnormally low body temperature?

I Who was the son of Daedalus?

J In the Bible who was the wife of Ahab?

K Which word of Japanese origin literally means 'divine wind'?

L *The Darling Buds of May* tells the story of which family?

M What name is given to the soft tissue in bone cavities?

QUIZ FOUR

N What name is given to a billionth of a second?

O Which brand of dentistry deals with correcting the position of teeth?

P What is the capital of Western Australia?

Q Which dish could be described as an egg tart?

R Who was the 40th President of the United States?

S In which town did Billy Butlin open his first holiday camp?

T What connects muscle to bone?

U What was the name of Thomas More's literary paradise?

V What name is given to the use of live animals for experiment?

W What is the male equivalent of a witch?

X Which five-letter word is the name of an African Bantu language?

Y Which cartoon character was described as the roughest, toughest hombre in the wild west?

Z What is the alternative name for a courgette?

ANSWERS
N. Nanosecond O. Orthodontics P. Perth Q. Quiche Lorraine R. Ronald Reagan S. Skegness T. Tendons U. Utopia V. Vivisection W. Warlock X. Xhosa Y. Yosemite Sam Z. Zucchini

QUIZ FIVE

A What is the most highly populated city in Alaska?

B What is the capital city of Switzerland?

C Which is the largest of the Carribean islands?

D Which African city is nicknamed 'The Pearl of the desert'?

E On which river does the city of Hamburg stand?

F What is the amicable nickname of Tonga?

G What is the name of the royal house in Monaco?

H In which country does a Magyar live?

I The city of Chicago lies in which state?

J Amman is the capital city of which country?

K What did Cambodia change its name to?

L Which song was a capital hit for the Clash in 1979?

M What is the capital city of Uruguay?

QUIZ FIVE

N Windhoek is the capital city of which country?

O What name is given to natives of the Orkneys?

P Which fruit is the national symbol of Spain?

Q What is the name of the mountain range that lies in the county of Somerset?

R What is the capital city of Iceland?

S A Salopian is a native of which English county?

T In which area of Romania was the home of Dracula?

U What is the capital city of Mongolia?

V What is the longest river in Europe?

W Which is the world's most southerly capital city?

X What is the name of the Amazon tributary that lies 320 kilometres (200 miles) from the Atlantic Ocean?

Y In which city was Dick Turpin hanged?

Z What is the alternative name for the Greek island of Zakynthos?

ANSWERS

N. Namibia O. Orcadian P. Pomegranate Q. Quantocks R. Reykjavik S. Shropshire T. Transylvania U. Ulan Bator V. Volga W. Wellington X. Xingu Y. York Z. Zante

QUIZ ONE

A Which is the largest breed of terrier?

B What word for a short jacket was also the title of a piece of music that you would associate with Torvill and Dean?

C Which football club dropped out of the Football League in the year 2000?

D In the year 2000 which former drummer for the Bay City Rollers stood trial on pornography charges?

E What name is given to the branch of philosophy concerned with human values?

F What name is given to the leaves of ferns?

G Where did the Campbells massacre the Macdonalds?

H 746 watts is equivalent to one what?

I What was the title of the sitcom in which Imelda Staunton played a solicitor?

J Who died on 2nd July 2000 after crashing his motorbike in Estonia?

K What word describes the speed of one nautical mile per hour?

L What was the name of the liner sunk by a German submarine on 7th May 1915?

M What is the name of the holiest city in the Islamic world?

ANSWERS

A. Airedale B. Bolero C. Chester D. Derek Longmuir E. Ethics F. Fronds G. Glen Coe H. Horsepower I. *Is It Legal?* J. Joey Dunlop K. Knot L. Lusitania M. Mecca

QUIZ ONE

N In the Bible who was described as a legendary hunter?

O How are Felix Unger and Oscar Madison collectively known?

P What is the name of Scotland's most easterly town?

Q Two pints make one what?

R What name is given to a teacher of Jewish law?

S What name is given to the highest order of angels?

T What would be your job if you stuffed animals for a living?

U Which mythical creature symbolises purity?

V What name is given to the soft hairy skin on a deer's antlers?

W Which children's toy wobbled but didn't fall down?

X What was the title of the album released by the rock group Iron Maiden in 1995?

Y Name the actor who played the leader of the original Magnificent Seven.

Z Which model of Ford car is also the name given to a soft, mild breeze?

QUIZ TWO

....

A What is the Islamic name of God?

B Which sport was invented by James Naismith?

C What name is given to the pupa of a butterfly?

D What eight-letter word is the name given to word blindness?

E Which short word is Latin for I?

F Who invented the jet engine?

G What name describes a gothic water spout usually in the form of a monster?

H Which of the Marx brothers was christened Arthur?

I What word describes the condition of being resistant to infection?

J What is the name of the cotton costume worn by judo competitors?

K Which word of Hindu origin literally means dust-coloured?

L What is the Latin word for liquid?

M What ruled China from 1368 to 1644?

QUIZ TWO

N What was the name of the French town where the sitcom *Allo, Allo* was set?

O What word is the name given to a piece of music that opens a concert?

P Which five-letter word means voting in place of another?

Q What would you spend in Guatemala?

R What is the name of the light-sensitive membrane at the back of the eye?

S Which mythical river led to Hades?

T What is the name of Saturn's largest moon?

U What word describes the sound waves that are above the range of the human ear?

V What form of black magic is practised on the island of Haiti?

W Aeolus is the Greek god of what?

X What was the registration of Gerry Anderson's Fireball piloted by Steve Zodiac?

Y What is the Tibetan word for snowman?

Z Which six-letter word is the name given to an extreme partisan?

ANSWERS

N. Nouvion O. Overture P. Proxy Q. Quetzal R. Retina S. Styx T. Titan U. Ultrasonic V. Voodoo W. Winds X. XL 5 Y. Yeti Z. Zealot

QUIZ THREE

A Which bone of the ear might be of particular interest to a blacksmith?

B What is the name of the arena in Sumo wrestling?

C Which war is most closely associated with Florence Nightingale?

D What name is given to the science of dating using tree rings?

E In April 2000 who was sacked as manager of Wimbledon FC?

F What is the female equivalent of the Davis Cup in tennis?

G What do Argentinians call cowboys?

H What did the Boulder Dam change its name to?

I What type of bird was sacred in Egypt?

J Which famous football team hails from Turin?

K Which country was invaded by Iraq in 1990?

L What name is given to a feet-first toboggan?

M What was the name of the race of tiny people that lived in the Emerald City?

ANSWERS

A. Anvil B. Basho C. Crimean D. Dendrochronology E. Egil Olsen F. Federation Cup G. Gauchos H. Hoover Dam I. Ibis J. Juventus K. Kuwait L. Luge M. Munchkins

QUIZ THREE

N What was invented by Wallace Carothers?

O What was the title of Michael Jackson's first UK No. 1 hit single?

P What is the official language of Afghanistan?

Q What was the surname of the infamous Norwegian traitor of World War II?

R What is the German word for empire?

S Which part of a flower produces the pollen?

T On which street is the Bank of England?

U What was the title of the No. 1 collaboration between Queen and David Bowie?

V What is the capital of Malta?

W What was the title of the 1960s sitcom that starred Jimmy Edwards as a teacher?

X What is the name of the major Mexican lake that contains ten letters?

Y What slang word is the name given to a golfer's nervous disability that affects his putting?

Z What is nicknamed Spice Island?

ANSWERS

N. Nylon O. 'One Day In Your Life' P. Pushtu Q. Quisling R. Reich S. Stamen T. Threadneedle U. 'Under Pressure' V. Valleta W. Whacko X. Xochimilco Y. Yipps Z. Zanzibar

QUIZ FOUR

A What is the alternative name for a Michaelmas daisy?

B What name is given to uncoined gold?

C What is the lowest female singing voice?

D What word describes the identification of an illness from its symptoms?

E What is the second book of the Bible?

F Mass x acceleration = ?

G What name is given to a castrated horse?

H 2.471 acres is equivalent to one what?

I What name is given to an isolated steep-sided hill?

J What was the title of the first 'talkie' film?

K What type of energy is described as motion energy?

L In which film did David Bowie play the king of the goblins?

M What name is given to a bishop's headgear?

ANSWERS
A. Aster. B. Bullion C. Contralto D. Diagnosis E. Exodus F. Force G. Gelding
H. Hectare I. Inselberg J. *Jazz Singer* K. Kinetic L. *Labyrinth* M. Mitre

42

QUIZ FOUR

N What was Bob Marley's middle name?

O 1997 was the Chinese year of the what?

P Which semi-circular instrument is used for measuring angles?

Q By what name is calcium oxide otherwise known?

R What is the surname of Sigourney Weaver's character in the Alien films?

S In golf what name is given to a No. 3 wood?

T Who was the sheriff of Four Feather Falls?

U Who narrates the Brer Rabbit stories?

V What was the name of Yuri Gagarin's spacecraft?

W What name is given to a dividing ridge between two river systems?

X Who does Lucy Lawless play on television?

Y What is the Sanskrit word for union?

Z The famous theme music for the film *The Third Man* was performed on what type of instrument?

QUIZ FIVE

....

A What sort of bird would you associate with three under in golf?

B Who was the Grand National winning jockey who sat astride Aldanti?

C What is the nickname of Norwich City FC?

D What is the name of the baseball team for Los Angeles?

E Which darts player is known as 'the crafty cockney'?

F What name is given to the style of high jump in which one jumps backwards over the pole?

G In which sport do teams contest the Sam Maguire Trophy?

H What is the name of the dance performed by the All Blacks rugby union team?

I Name the Swedish boxer who became World Heavyweight Champion in 1959.

J Who was the first ever man to swim 100 metres in less than one minute?

K Which famous name from the world of football had a hit record with a song called 'Head Over Heels In Love'?

L Which golfer acquired the nickname 'Supermex'?

M Who was the Men's Singles Champion at Wimbledon in 1991?

QUIZ FIVE

N What do jockeys and trainers refer to as HQ?

O What is the name of Houston's American Football team?

P Who were cricket World Champions in 1992?

Q Which horse won the Epsom Derby in 1990?

R In which sport is the Britannia Cup contested?

S What is the name of the winter sports venue that is home to the famous Cresta Run?

T In which sporting activity would you perform a randolph?

U What is the name of West Ham United FC's home ground?

V Which famous tennis player has a sister called Serena?

W What is the nickname of Australia's rugby union team?

X Who was ranked Belgium's No. 1 tennis player in 2000?

Y Which sport involves ducking the boom?

Z What is the name of the Dutch Grand Prix venue?

ANSWERS

N. Newmarket O. Oilers P. Pakistan Q. Quest for Fame R. Rowing S. St Moritz T. Trampolining U. Upton Park V. Venus Williams W. Wallabies X. Xavier Malisse Y. Yachting Z. Zandvoort

QUIZ ONE

A What name is given to the spongy tissue between the back of the nose and throat?

B What is the surname of the man credited with inventing the computer?

C What is added to steel to make it stainless?

D In the *Eagle* comic who was known as the pilot of the future?

E What is the alternative name for the North American moose?

F What name is given to a litter of piglets?

G What name is given to a Japanese dancing girl?

H A swedge is a tool used for making what?

I In American police forces which department is known by the initials I A?

J By what name is the villain Jack Napier otherwise known?

K What is the name of the hypnotic python in *The Jungle Book*?

L What four-letter word describes the brand emblem of a company?

M Who was Lady Chatterley's lover?

QUIZ ONE

N Saint Agatha is the patron saint of which profession?

O Who was Shakespeare's Moor of Venice?

P What was the name of the royal house of Henry II?

Q Which Latin phrase means wanting something in exchange for something else?

R There are 500 sheets of paper in a what?

S Which is the world's oldest auctioneers?

T James T Kirk. What does the T stand for?

U What is the alternative name for the star constellation known as the Great Bear?

V What was the name of the Flemish painter who gave his name to a style of beard?

W What name is given to the French-speaking population of Belgium?

X How is ninety written in Roman numerals?

Y Which film told the life story of George Cohen?

Z Who infamously tripped Mary Decker in 1984?

ANSWERS

N. Nurses O. Othello P. Plantagenet Q. Quid pro quo R. Ream S. Sothebys T. Tiberius U. Ursa Major V. Van Dyck W. Walloons X. XC Y. Yankee Doodle Dandy Z. Zola Budd

QUIZ TWO

A Who is the Greek goddess of love and beauty?

B What was the name of the village that witnessed the Charge of the Light Brigade?

C What name is given to a dish of chicken, bacon and red wine?

D What is the name of the first portion of the stomach?

E How was the TV character of Robert McCall advertised in a newspaper?

F Which surname connects Henry, Jane, Peter and Bridget?

G What comes between conception and birth?

H What shape is an ice crystal?

I What name is given to the period of hatching out of eggs?

J Who invented the aqualung?

K What is one hundredth of a rouble?

L What type of garment is a dhoti?

M Which footballer won the World Cup's Golden Boot in 1978?

ANSWERS

A. Aphrodite B. Balaclava C. Coq au vin D. Duodenum E. Equaliser F. Fonda
G. Gestation H. Hexagonal I. Incubation J. Jacques Cousteau K. Kopeck L. Loincloth
M. Mario Kempes

QUIZ TWO

N Which American city is known as the birthplace of jazz?

O What is the singular of opera?

P What name is given to the study of rocks?

Q What was the name of Manfred Mann's mighty Eskimo?

R Where was the Magna Carta signed?

S What name is given to a broad brimmed Mexican hat?

T What name is given to the person who is making a will?

U Who provided the backing for the singer Gary Puckett?

V Who composed the theme for the film *Chariots of Fire*?

W Who was the longest-serving England football manager of the 20th century?

X What name was given to the typhoon that killed 19 people in the Philippines in October 2000?

Y What is the opposite of Yang?

Z What is the name of the largest island of Denmark?

ANSWERS
N. New Orleans O. Opus P. Petrology Q. Quinn R. Runnymede S. Sombrero T. Testator U. Union Gap V. Vangelis W. Walter Winterbottom X. Xangsane Y. Yin Z. Zealand

49

QUIZ THREE

A In which city was the world's first contraceptive clinic opened?

B Which sport is mentioned in the Shakespeare play *Antony and Cleopatra*?

C On 10th January 2000 who was fined at Luton train station for failing to buy a ticket?

D What does a drodometer measure?

E Which model of Ford car did Henry Ford name after his son?

F What is the capital city of the island of Martinique?

G Which golfer is known as the Great White Shark?

H What is the longest bridge in Britain?

I In which country is the Negev desert?

J What does the J stand for in the name of the author J K Rowling?

K Which commentator spoke the famous words 'They think it's all over it is now'?

L What name is given to the home of a wolf?

M What game would a player be playing if he rolled his bonce at an alley?

QUIZ THREE

N What is the name of Frasier Crane's brother in the American sitcom?

O What is nicknamed the City of Dreaming Spires?

P What name is given to the manufacture of artificial limbs?

Q What name is given to a square dance involving four couples?

R Which car manufacturer has made models called the Mégane and the Dauphine?

S What would you be eating if you dined on calamari?

T Which Shropshire town was named after a famous engineer?

U Which actress danced with John Travolta in the film *Pulp Fiction*?

V What was the title of the best-seller written by Jacqueline Susann?

W What is the American equivalent of the *Financial Times*?

X What name is given to the morbid fear of deserts?

Y What song was a No. 1 hit for the pop duo Baccara?

Z What is the name of the venue which hosts the Chinese Grand Prix?

ANSWERS

N. Niles O. Oxford P. Prosthetics Q. Quadrille R. Renault S. Squid T. Telford U. Uma Thurman V. *Valley of the Dolls* W. *Wall Street Journal* X. Xerophobia Y. 'Yes Sir I Can Boogie' Z. Zhuhai

5

QUIZ FOUR

A How is the thyroid cartilage better known?

B What name has been given to fifteen different Popes?

C What name is given to a group of cats?

D What type of doctor specialises in diseases of the skin?

E What name is given to the occasion when the sun lies directly above the Equator?

F Which group had a sixties hit with the song 'Let's Go To San Francisco'?

G Who played Arnold in the sitcom *Different Strokes*?

H Which king was victorious at the Battle of Bosworth Field?

I What name can be given to a whole or natural number?

J What did Joseph Cyril Bamford invent?

K Who was Gene Wilder's woman in red?

L What is the lightest known metal?

M Which Leicestershire town is famous for its pork pies?

ANSWERS

A. Adam's apple B. Benedict C. Clowder D. Dermatologist E. Equinox F. Flowerpot Men G. Gary Coleman H. Henry VII I. Integer J. JCB K. Kelly le Brock L. Lithium M. Melton Mowbray

QUIZ FOUR

N In which American state is Las Vegas?

O Who directed the film *JFK*?

P What was the name of the first Blue Peter dog?

Q What name is given to the cornerstone of a building?

R What is the Sanskrit word for kingdom?

S Which is the only sea on the planet with no coastline?

T Which element is represented by the chemical symbol W?

U What was founded on October 24th 1945?

V What name is given to a cycling stadium?

W In which road would you find the former headquarters of the Labour Party?

X What did Malcolm Little change his name to?

Y What name is given to a Grand Champion?

Z Who was the youngest of the Marx brothers?

ANSWERS

N. Nevada O. Oliver Stone P. Petra Q. Quoin R. Raj S. Sargasso Sea T. Tungsten U. United Nations V. Velodrome W. Walworth X. Malcolm Y. Yokozuna Z. Zeppo

QUIZ FIVE

....

A What is the title of the film in which Bruce Willis plays an oil driller called Harry Stamper?

B In which 1980 film did Robert Redford play a liberal prison governor?

C What was the title of the film in which Laurence Oliver played Zeus, the king of the Greek gods?

D Which screen villain was played in 1962 by Joseph Wiseman?

E Which film told the true story of John Merrick?

F In which 1940 film did Mickey Mouse play the Sorcerer's Apprentice?

G Which film earned Ben Kingsley a Best Actor Oscar?

H In which film did Sean Connery advise Christopher Lambert that there could only be one?

I Peter Sellers played a militant representative called Fred Kite in which film?

J What was the title of the film that starred Robin Williams and featured a spectacular jungle stampede?

K Elvis Presley played a New Orleans nightclub singer in which film?

L What was the title of the film in which Kirk Douglas played Vincent Van Gogh?

M Alan Parker directed Gene Hackman in which film concerning Klu Klux Klan activities?

ANSWERS

A. Armageddon B. Brubaker C. Clash Of The Titans D. Dr No E. Elephant Man
F. Fantasia G. Ghandi H. Highlander I. I'm All right Jack J. Jumanji K. Kid Creole L. Lust For
Life M. Mississippi burning

QUIZ FIVE

N Where did Hugh Grant fall in love with Julia Roberts?

O What was the title of the film for which Marlon Brando won his first Best Actor Oscar?

P Harrison Ford was accused of murdering Greta Scacchi in which 1990 film?

Q Which 1990 film was set in Australia and starred Tom Selleck in the title role?

R Who has been played on film by Errol Flynn, John Cleese, Patrick Bergin and Kevin Costner?

S In which film did Pauline Collins leave her husband to fly to the island of Mykonos?

T What was the title of the 1999 Mike Leigh film, which told the story of Gilbert and Sullivan?

U Macauley Culkin played the nephew of John Candy in which 1989 film?

V Which 1960 film was based on the novel *The Midwich Cuckoos*?

W The Jets opposed the Sharks in which musical?

X Which 2000 film stars Patrick Stewart as Dr X?

Y Which 1983 film was set in Poland and starred Barbra Streisand as a Jewish girl who tries to get on in the world by dressing as a boy?

Z Which film tells the story of the Battle of Rourke's Drift?

ANSWERS

N. Notting Hill O. On The Waterfront P. Presumed Innocent Q. Quigley Down Under R. Robin Hood S. Shirley Valentine T. Topsy Turvy U. Uncle Buck V. Village Of The Damned W. West Side Story X. X Men Y. Yentl Z. Zulu

QUIZ ONE

A What name is given to the white of an egg?

B What was the name of the white-suited politician in the TV series *The Dukes of Hazzard*?

C What title is given to an officer who sees to an army's provisions?

D What would your job be if you dealt in cloth?

E In 1996 which nation failed to turn up for an international football match against Scotland?

F What is the technical term for a tightrope walker?

G 4.56 litres is equivalent to what?

H What name is given to the type of long, heavy moustache that curls up at both ends?

I What metallic nickname was bestowed upon Margaret Thatcher?

J Which religious group was founded by Ignatius de Loyola?

K In which city did General Gordon die?

L What is Lovejoy's first name?

M 'House of Fun' was the only No. 1 hit for which group?

ANSWERS

A. Albumen B. Boss Hogg C. Commissary D. Draper E. Estonia F. Funambulist G. Gallon H. Handlebar I. Iron Lady J. Jesuits K. Khartoum L. Lothario M. Madness

QUIZ ONE

N What name is given to a piece of music describing a night scene?

O What is the Greek word for a theatre?

P Which stage musical featured the song 'All I Ask of You'?

Q Which game involves the throwing of iron rings?

R What is the currency unit of Pakistan?

S What was the nationality of the referee in the 1966 football Word Cup Final?

T What name is given to a Red Indian's war axe?

U Which song that was a hit for the pop group Squeeze told the story of a girl from Clapham?

V What name is given to the left hand page of a book?

W Which American state is nicknamed the 'equality state'?

X How is sixteen written in Roman numerals?

Y What was the name of the 1945 conference attended by Churchill, Roosevelt and Stalin?

Z What is the name of the holy hill of Jerusalem?

ANSWERS
N. Nocturne O. Odeon P. *Phantom Of The Opera* Q. Quoits R. Rupee S. Swiss T. Tomahawk U. 'Up The Junction' V. Verso W. Wyoming X. XVI Y. Yalta Conference Z. Zion

QUIZ TWO

A Which is the thickest tendon in the human body?

B What musical instrument is affectionately known as 'the gentleman of the woodwinds'?

C The Tivoli amusement park is found in which city?

D Which song was a No.1 hit for U2 in 1988?

E Who wrote the novel *Brideshead Revisited*?

F Which projectile was invented by Fred Morrison?

G What is the second word on a George Cross?

H What name is given to the winter dormancy of animals?

I What did the Dutch East Indies change their name to?

J Who is the mother of Jamie Lee Curtis?

K What name is given to the knife of a Gurkha?

L On which river does Dublin stand?

M By what name is a groundhog also known?

ANSWERS

A. Achilles B. Bassoon C. Copenhagen D.'Desire' E. Evelyn Waugh F. Frisbee G. Gallantry H. Hibernation I. Indonesia J. Janet Leigh K. Kukri L. Liffey M. Marmot

QUIZ TWO

N What is added to stainless steel to make it tougher?

O Which national drink of Greece has an aniseed taste?

P What name is given to a group of owls?

Q What is the name of New York's largest borough?

R In which town was the first Co-operative Society established?

S The Antiguan racer is the world's rarest species of what?

T What name is given to the medical procedure that involves the drilling of a hole in the skull?

U In America what is known as the Mormon state?

V If canine refers to dogs which word refers to foxes?

W Which former British Prime Minister was known as 'the grand old man'?

X What is the medical term for the abnormal dryness of bodily tissues?

Y In the novel *Gulliver's Travels* what was the name of the race of humans that were ruled by horses?

Z Which villain was played by Christopher Walken in the Bond film *A View To A Kill*?

ANSWERS

N. Nickel O. Ouzo P. Parliament Q. Queens R. Rochdale S. Snake T. Trepanning U. Utah V. Vulpine W. William Gladstone X. Xerosis Y. Yahoos Z. Zorin

QUIZ THREE

A What is measured by an altimeter?

B What is a male rabbit called?

C What old unit of measurement was equivalent to 18 inches?

D What is a female rabbit called?

E Whose autobiography is entitled *My Wicked, Wicked Ways*?

F What type of acid is present in nettle stings?

G What was the name of Fletcher's cellmate in the sitcom *Porridge*?

H How is pyrosis more commonly known?

I Which sport star's autobiography is called *All Round View*?

J Who wrote the novel *The Secret Life Of Walter Mitty*?

K What word is derived from the German for children's garden?

L On TV who played Steve Austin?

M Which city played host to the 1976 Summer Olympics?

QUIZ THREE

N What name is given to the study of clouds?

O What is the surname of Boy George?

P What name is given to a castle door that opens vertically?

Q What was the former name of the Beatles?

R What was the French word for a meeting place?

S On which hill was the Battle of Hastings fought?

T What is the birthstone for November?

U In Greek mythology who killed the Cyclops?

V What was discovered by Dumond D'Urville on the island of Melos?

W What is the name of the small beetle that destroys grain?

X What is the fourteenth letter of the Greek alphabet?

Y Who played the female half of George & Mildred?

Z What name is given to a seven-stage watch tower?

ANSWERS
N. Nephology O. O'Dowd P. Portcullis Q. Quarrymen R. Rendezvous S. Senlac
T. Topaz U. Ulysses V. Venus de Milo W. Weevil X. Xi Y. Yootha Joyce Z. Ziggurat

QUIZ FOUR

A What is the name of the world's highest waterfall?

B What is the name of Russia's premier ballet company?

C What are the smallest blood vessels in the body called?

D What is sound intensity measured in?

E What is 29,028 feet high?

F In which film did Burt Lancaster play Sergeant Warden?

G What is the smallest species of ape?

H What does an American call a tramp?

I What was the former name of JFK airport?

J What was the name of the only sea battle of World War II ?

K What is the name of the holy book of Islam?

L What is the longest river in France?

M Who is the Roman goddess of wisdom?

QUIZ FOUR

N Whom did Robert Wagner marry on two separate occasions?

O What is the anatomical term for the gullet?

P Who picked a peck of pickled pepper?

Q Which song made famous by Doris Day first featured in the film *The Man Who Knew Too Much*?

R Who wrote 'Auld Lang Syne'?

S What is bladderwrack a type of?

T What was the name of Roy Rogers's horse?

U Kiev is the capital of which country?

V What is the nickname of Port Vale FC?

W In which town is *Dad's Army* set?

X A marimba is a type of which musical instrument?

Y In which sitcom did Paul Eddington play Jim Hacker?

Z What was the name of the lion in the *Wizard Of Oz*?

ANSWERS

N. Natalie Wood O. Oesophagus P. Peter Piper Q. 'Que Sera Sera' R. Robert Burns S. Seaweed T. Trigger U. Ukraine V. Valiants W. Walmington on Sea X. Xylophone Y. Yes, *Prime Minister* (formerly Yes, *Minister*) Z. Zeke

QUIZ FIVE

Identify the 26 words from their quick fire definitions.

A To withhold a vote.

B Russian guitar.

C The art of beautiful handwriting.

D District under the jurisdiction of a bishop.

E The study of insects.

F The wire in a light bulb.

G A Venetian canal boat.

H A sailors' lively dance.

I Coloured part of the eye.

J Chinese sailing ship.

K Loose breeches tucked in at the knee.

L The voice box.

M Colour between pink and red.

ANSWERS

A. Abstain B. Balalaika C. Calligraphy D. Diocese E. Entomology F. Filament G. Gondola H. Hornpipe I. Iris J. Junk K. Knickerbockers L. Larynx M. Magenta

QUIZ FIVE

N A lump of gold.

O Egg shaped.

P Broad, level stretch of high land.

Q Any four-footed animal.

R Pertaining to the countryside.

S Half man, half goat.

T The study of poisons.

U To seize and hold without right.

V The blade of a windmill.

W Old-fashioned word for anti-clockwise.

X A three-masted pirate vessel.

Y A pair of oxen.

Z The highest point.

SESSION 7

QUIZ ONE

A Which radio soap is set on Brookfield farm?

B What is the name of the Brontë sisters' brother?

C What ran from Cincinnati to New Orleans?

D Which bird became extinct in 1681?

E What was the name of Bruce Springsteen's backing band?

F What was the name of the legendary ghost ship said to haunt the Cape of Good Hope?

G What is the name of the first spacecraft to orbit Jupiter?

H Which species of eagle is the world's largest bird of prey?

I What was the surname of the judge at the O J Simpson trial?

J Who is married to Ade Edmondson?

K What name is given to a smoked herring?

L Who carried out a naked protest against taxes imposed by her husband Leofric?

M What name is given to a double-sized bottle of champagne?

ANSWERS
A. *Archers* B. Branwell C. Chatanooga Choo Choo D. Dodo E. E Street Band F. Flying *Dutchman* G. *Galileo* H. Harpy I. Ito J. Jennifer Saunders K. Kipper L. Lady Godiva M. Magnum

QUIZ ONE

N What name is given to the tubes in the kidneys?

O What is the Japanese art of paper-folding called?

P Prunus Domestica is the scientific name for a what?

Q Which current affairs TV programme has been hosted by Sir Robin Day and David Dimbleby?

R What was the name of Alexander the Great's wife?

S Name the actress who played the title role in the film *Carrie*?

T On whose TV show did the Simpsons make their television debut?

U According to the nursery rhyme where did Little Boy Blue fall fast asleep?

V Which woman has appeared on the front cover of *Time* magazine the most often?

W What symbol represents the star sign of Aquarius?

X Which pop group were making plans for Nigel?

Y Aden is the capital city of where?

Z What name is given to the rind of a lemon?

ANSWERS

N. Nephrons O. Origami P. Plum Q. *Question Time* R. Roxana S. Sissy Spacek T. Tracy Ullman U. Under the haystack V. Virgin Mary W. Water Carrier X. XTC Y. Yemen Z. Zest

QUIZ TWO

A Which six-letter word is the name given to an enclosure for birds?

B What is the home city of Manuel in *Fawlty Towers*?

C What is the former name of Istanbul?

D What name is given to the triangular shaped piece of land at the mouth of a river?

E Which Nobel prize was instituted in 1969?

F Vitu Levu is the largest island in which island group?

G In which city does Batman fight crime?

H Which cowboy rode a horse called Topper?

I In which country was Katie Boyle born?

J What is the first name of Inspector Clouseau?

K Which sitcom features the character of Hyacinth Bucket?

L Who is credited with inventing jeans?

M What is the capital of the Philippines?

QUIZ TWO

N Which literary character married Madeline Bray?

O On which lake does the city of Toronto stand?

P Who did Don Warrington play in *Rising Damp*?

Q What seven-letter word is the name of a sacred Aztec bird?

R What does an herpetologist study?

S By what six-letter nickname is Daniel Hooper better known?

T Who played Magnum PI?

U What does a cosmologist study?

V Andrew Fitzgibbon, aged 15, is the youngest recipient of a what?

W Who was the first ever president of the England Bowls Association?

X To which group of fruits does a coconut belong?

Y What type of tree is often found in churchyards?

Z In which city is the headquarters of FIFA?

QUIZ THREE

A How did the Queen refer to the year 1992?

B Where is the gluteus maximus muscle located?

C In which country did General Pinochet launch a military coup in 1973?

D In golf what name is given to a No. 1 wood?

E Who composed the theme music for *Coronation Street*?

F In which novel does Bathsheba Everdene marry Sergeant Troy and Gabriel Oak?

G What six-letter word is the name given to a picturesque cave?

H In which city is the headquarters of the International Court of Justice?

I In which film did Daniel Day-Lewis play Gerry Donlon?

J At the 1998 Brit Awards Danbert Nobacon tipped a bucket of water over who?

K What is the main currency unit of Denmark?

L What name is given to the lines that supposedly link prehistoric sites?

M 2004 will be the Chinese year of the what?

QUIZ THREE

N What is the fourth book of the Bible?

O In June 1973 the first students graduated from where?

P On TV who played Edna the Inebriated Woman?

Q Which equine creature is an extinct relative of the zebra?

R Which blood factor was named after a species of monkey?

S Which day precedes Ash Wednesday?

T What was discovered in 1922 by Howard Carter?

U What is the name of the central character in the novel *Last Of The Mohicans*?

V In the TV programme *Falcon Crest*, what was Falcon Crest?

W In which river did the Pied Piper drown the rats of Hamelin?

X How many points is the letter X worth in Scrabble?

Y Hebe is the Greek goddess of what?

Z Which country has a name that literally means house of stone?

ANSWERS

N. Numbers O. Open University P. Patricia Hayes Q. Quagga R. Rhesus S. Shrove Tuesday T. Tutankhamun's tomb U. Uncas V. Vineyard W. Weser X. Eight Y. Youth Z. Zimbabwe

QUIZ FOUR

A Which actress was voted Rear of the Year in 1987?

B Shane Lynch of Boyzone has a twin in which pop group?

C In which sport would you soop the ice?

D What is the name of the chief respiratory muscle?

E How was Rodrigo diaz de Vivar better known?

F What name is given to non-identical twins?

G Which city was the 1990 European City of Culture?

H What was the name of Steptoe & Son's horse?

I Who wrote the novel *Rich Man, Poor Man*?

J Who became WBF World Heavyweight Boxing Champion at the ripe old age of 48?

K What is the collective name for a group of kittens?

L By what name is clarified edible pig fat better known?

M What colour of car is exclusively reserved for members of the Japanese imperial family?

ANSWERS

A. Anita Dobson B. Bewitched C. Curling D. Diaphragm E. El Cid F. Fraternal G. Glasgow H. Hercules I. Irwin Shaw J. Joe Bugner K. Kindle L. Lard M. Maroon

QUIZ FOUR

N Which city is served by Jomo Kenyatta airport?

O Which film earned Robert Redford an Oscar as Best Director?

P A daguerreotype was an early form of what?

Q What six-letter word is the name of a painful disease of the throat?

R Which golfing event was first contested in 1927?

S In which city is Bondi Beach?

T Which part of the body is affected by glossitis?

U In America it is called *College Bowl*. What is the name of this TV programme in Britain?

V By what title is the sitcom character Geraldine Grainger also known?

W Which 1962 film told the story of the Hudson sisters?

X Which opera with five letters in its title was composed by Handel?

Y What is Fred Flintstone's favourite cry of elation?

Z What name is given to the dish of egg yolks with marsala?

QUIZ FIVE

A On which singer's TV show did the Osmonds make their TV debut?

B What was the name of the first test pilot of Concorde who died in March 2001?

C Who is the actress daughter of Debbie Reynolds?

D Which TV chef became director of Norwich City FC?

E Which pop superstar married Renata Blauel?

F Who was nicknamed the Lady With The Lamp?

G Who led the group the Tubeway Army?

H In the year 2000 which model did Paul McCartney introduce as his new girlfriend?

I Who was backed by the Blockheads?

J Whose last words were "Et tu Brute"?

K On TV who plays Norah Batty?

L What was the name of the snooker referee who crushed a snooker ball with his bare hands in an advert for Carling Black Label?

M Who was the youngest recipient of the Nobel Peace Prize in the 20th century?

QUIZ FIVE

N Which singer had hits in the 1980s with 'The Riddle' and 'Wide Boy'?

O Which soul singer died in a plane crash in December 1967?

P Who shot and killed Billy the Kid?

Q Who was the naked civil servant?

R Which Hollywood actor became the father-in-law of John McEnroe?

S In the world of football who was known as the wizard of dribble?

T On TV who played the private eye Eddie Shoestring?

U Who was the first Bond girl?

V In World War II who became known as the sweetheart of the forces?

W Which actor played Passenger 57 on film?

X What was the name of the wife of Socrates?

Y Who was the second wife of John Lennon?

Z In the year 2000 who was voted Radio 1 Personality of the Year?

ANSWERS

N. Nik Kershaw O. Otis Redding P. Pat Garrett Q. Quentin Crisp R. Ryan O'Neal S. Stanley Matthews T. Trevor Eve U. Ursula Andress V. Vera Lynn W. Wesley Snipes X. Xanthippe Y. Yoko Ono Z. Zoe Ball

SESSION 8

QUIZ ONE

A Who won the men's London Marathon in the year 2000?

B What was the stage name of the horror movie star Williams Henry Pratt?

C What is the state capital of Wyoming?

D Who wrote about the amorous adventures of Moll Flanders?

E 350, Fifth Avenue, New York is the official address of which building?

F What did Charles Dickens refer to as a London particular?

G Which screen monster lived on Odo Island?

H The word amen originated in which language?

I Which is the 14th wedding anniversary?

J When Edward Hardwicke played Dr Watson, who played Sherlock Holmes?

K In the song 'Waltzing Matilda', what is a matilda?

L In which Egyptian city would you find the Valley of the Kings?

M What did Robert Burns refer to as 'a wee sleekit, cow'rin, tim'rous beastie'?

QUIZ ONE

N Who did Robert Vaughan play in *The Man From UNCLE*?

O Where are the Bislett Games held?

P What name is given to a field that rice grows in?

Q Doha is the capital city of which country?

R Who was the leader of the Gunpowder Plot?

S Which Beatles song did Frank Sinatra describe as the greatest love song of the last forty years?

T What is the name the Famous Five's dog?

U Which film company took over MGM in the 1970s?

V What name is given to rust on copper?

W What is the official national sport of Bulgaria?

X What is the chemical symbol for xenon?

Y What five-letter word is the name given to a country bumpkin?

Z Which pop duo hit the top of the charts with the song 'In The Year 2525'?

ANSWERS

N. Napoleon Solo O. Oslo P. Paddy field Q. Qatar R. Robert Catesby
S. 'Something' T. Timmy U. United Artists V. Verdigris W. Weight-lifting X. Xe Y. Yokel
Z. Zager & Evans

QUIZ TWO

A Which hormone stimulates the nervous system and raises the heart rate?

B What name is given to the straps placed around a horse's head?

C Which is the only member of the cat family that does not have retractable claws?

D Excluding Oxford and Cambridge which is the oldest University in England?

E What was the name of the UFO prophet in the sitcom *Mork and Mindy*?

F Which literary character has a wife called Mildew and a son called Mold?

G Which cheese was named after a small town near Milan?

H Which chain-store was founded by Terence Conran?

I What name is given to the signs or badges showing that one holds an office?

J What type of large vehicle was named after a Hindu god?

K How is August Darnelle known when he is playing with his coconuts?

L In which crime drama did Samantha Janus play a detective constable?

M Alan Hope became the first person to win a by-election for which party?

ANSWERS

A. Adrenaline B. Bridle C. Cheetah D. Durham E. Exidor F. Fungus the Bogeyman G. Gorgonzola H. Habitat I. Insignia J. Juggernaut K. Kid Creole L. Liverpool One M. Monster Raving Loony Party

QUIZ TWO

N Catherine Morland is the heroine in which novel?

O What name is given to the science of correcting deformities of the skeleton?

P What sort of birds would congregate in a covey?

Q What was the surname of President George Bush Snr's Vice President?

R In the 1999 TV adaptation of *Oliver Twist*, who played Fagan?

S In America what was abolished by the 13th Amendment?

T What is the lowest-pitched brass musical instrument?

U What is the anatomical name for the womb?

V Who liked the Remington shaver so much he bought the company?

W If a face was describe as rugose what would it be?

X What was invented by Chester Carlson?

Y Which fashion designer promoted the little girl look?

Z What is the name of the highest mountain in Germany?

ANSWERS
N. *Northanger Abbey* O. Orthopaedics P. Partridges Q. Quayle R. Robert Lindsay S. Slavery T. Tuba U. Uterus V. Victor Kiam W. Wrinkled X. Xerox Y. Yves St Laurent Z. Zugspitze

QUIZ THREE

A What are the air sacs called that are contained within the lungs?

B What are the thick layers of fat under the skin of whales called?

C There are twenty-three pairs of what in the human body?

D Which song was a No. 1 hit for Right Said Fred?

E Who sculpted the lions in Trafalgar Square?

F Which novel is sub-titled *Or The Modern Prometheus*?

G In which film did Demi Moore shave her head to join the US Navy Seals?

H What registers as 12 on the Beaufort Scale?

I What is the 6th colour of the rainbow?

J On April 26th 1999 who was found murdered on Gowan Avenue?

K Which act won the Eurovision Song Contest in 1997?

L The intensity of what is measured by a photometer?

M What nationality is the snooker star Tony Drago?

ANSWERS

A. Alveoli B. Blubber C. Chromosomes D. Deeply Dippy E. Edwin Landseer F. *Frankenstein* G. *GI Jane* H. Hurricane I. Indigo J. Jill Dando K. Katrina and the Waves L. Light M. Maltese

QUIZ THREE

N In which country was Bianca Jagger born?

O Who created Ivor the Engine?

P A Welsh cob is a breed of what?

Q What is the radio call-sign for the letter Q?

R According to Boney M who was Russia's greatest love machine?

S What title was given to Japanese military rulers between the 12th and 19th centuries?

T Green, Oolong and Orange Pekoe are all types of what?

U In which 1992 film was Jean Claude Van Damme transformed into a robotic soldier?

V Which song topped the charts for Madonna in 1990?

W Who was the first Norman monarch of England?

X What name is given to a plant that can withstand drought conditions?

Y What breed of dog was the Cruft's Supreme Champion in 1997?

Z What do Americans call a facial spot?

ANSWERS
N. Nicaragua O. Oliver Postgate P. Pony Q. Quebec R. Rasputin S. Shogun T. Tea U. *Universal Soldier* V. 'Vogue' W. William the Conqueror X. Xerophyte Y. Yorkshire Terrier Z. Zit

QUIZ FOUR

A For what crime was Anne Boleyn beheaded?

B What was the maiden name of the Queen Mother?

C What method of child delivery was named after a Roman Emperor?

D In which American city would you find the famous Kronk boxing gymnasium?

E What is the name of the nearest forest to London?

F Which horse won the Grand National in 1967 at the remarkable odds of 100-1?

G If pamplemousse was ordered in a French restaurant, what would arrive?

H What was the name of the nine-headed monster killed by Hercules?

I Which song was a hit for the Small Faces and M People?

J In which film did Arnold Schwarzenegger fall pregnant?

K Who won the Best Actor Oscar in the year 2000?

L What would be the destination of luggage labelled LOS?

M Which actress married the playwright Jack Rosenthal?

ANSWERS
A. Adultery B. Bowes-Lyon C. Caesarian D. Detroit E. Epping Forest F. Foinhaven G. Grapefruit H. Hydra I. 'Itchycoo Park' J. Junior' K. Kevin Spacey L. Lagos M. Maureen Lipman

QUIZ FOUR

N Under what name did Noah Kaminsky sell millions of records around the world?

O What is the literal English translation of Sinn Fein?

P What breed of dog was Ethel Skinner's Willy in EastEnders?

Q Which group was fronted by Paul Young early in his pop career?

R What name is given to a herring served with an onion?

S Which No. I hit for Rod Stewart was written by Gavin Sutherland?

T What name is given to a locked stand for spirit bottles?

U If dog = canine, what word = bear?

V What is the Italian word for wasp?

W What sort of creature is Chewbacca in the *Star Wars* films?

X Which 1982 film tells the story of a woman impregnated by an alien?

Y Rick Wakeman played the keyboards in which group?

Z On which river does the Kariba Dam stand?

ANSWERS

N. Neil Diamond O. Ourselves alone P. Pug Q. Q Tips R. Rollmop S. 'Sailing' T. Tantalus U. Ursine V. Vespa W. Wookey X. Xtro Y. Yes Z. Zambezi

QUIZ FIVE

A Who did Smokie live next door to for twenty-four years?

B Which song written by Carl Perkins was a hit for Elvis Presley in 1956?

C Neil Kinnock, Margaret Thatcher, Lester Piggott, Paul Daniels, Ronald Reagan and many others appeared in the video for which 1986 No. 1 hit?

D In which song did 10cc claim that they did not like reggae?

E Which flower did Christopher Plummer sing about in *The Sound of Music*?

F What was the first song to be sung in the musical *Oliver*?

G Which song provided Clive Dunn with an unexpected No. 1 hit?

H Which song contains the line 'Flies are in your pea soup baby, they're waving at me'?

I What was the first song to top the single charts for the Rolling Stones?

J What Rolf Harris song character possessed an extra leg?

K Which song has been a hit for Eddie Floyd, Otis Redding, Amii Stewart and David Bowie?

L Who invented the medicinal compound?

M Which song from the musical *Cats* was a hit for Elaine Paige and opened with the word Midnight?

ANSWERS

A. Alice B. 'Blue Suede Shoes' C. 'Chicken Song' D. 'Dreadlock Holiday' E. 'Edelweiss'
F. 'Food, Glorious Food' G. 'Grandad' H. 'Hi Ho Silver Lining' I. 'It's All Over Now'
J. 'Jake the Peg' K. 'Knock On Wood' L. 'Lily The Pink' M. 'Memory'

QUIZ FIVE

N Which song has been a hit for Gloria Gaynor and the Communards?

O Which song from the musical *Showboat* was inspired by the Mississippi?

P What was the only No. 1 hit for Musical Youth?

Q Which playing card was a disco hit for K C and the Sunshine Band?

R Which song first released in 1957 took almost 29 years to reach No. 1?

S What was Abba's last No. 1 in the UK?

T Which one-word song title has been a hit for Shirley Bassey, the Move, the Rubettes, Kool and the Gang, David Bowie, Def Leppard, Boomtown Rats and New Kids on the Block?

U What sort of bird provided the actor Mike Reid with a top 10 hit?

V Which type of very hot food gave Fat Les a No. 2 hit in 1998?

W What was Lee Marvin born under?

X Which song was a No. 1 collaboration for Olivia Newton John and the Electric Light Orchestra?

Y What is the most recorded song of all time?

Z Which song from the film *The Song of the South* was nominated for Best Song Oscar?

ANSWERS

N. 'Never Can Say Goodbye' O. 'Ol' Man River' P. 'Pass the Dutchie' Q. Queen of Clubs R. 'Reet Petite' S. 'Super Trouper' T. 'Tonight' U. 'Ugly Duckling' V. 'Vindaloo' W. 'Wanderin' Star' X. 'Xanadu' Y. 'Yesterday' Z. 'Zip-A-Dee-Doo-Dah'

QUIZ ONE

A Who founded the Body Shop?

B What breed of dog was Snoopy?

C Which sitcom features a restaurant called Le Chateau Anglais?

D What is the name of the index of prices on the New York stock exchange?

E Which notorious plane provided the title of a Top 10 hit for OMD?

F Who was the first singer to have three UK No. 1 hits in one year?

G According to the legend where is King Arthur buried?

H What was rebuilt and reopened as the King Baudouin Stadium?

I Djakarta is the capital city of where?

J What did the Gregorian calendar replace?

K Who became the first female Prime Minister of Canada?

L Which Dallas character was nicknamed The Poison Dwarf by Terry Wogan?

M Cornflakes are made from which cereal?

ANSWERS

A. Anita Roddick B. Beagle C. *Chef* D. Dow Jones E. Enola Gay F. Frankie Laine G. Glastonbury H. Heysel Stadium I. Indonesia J. Julian calendar K. Kim Campbell L. Lucy Ewing M. Maize

QUIZ ONE

N In mythology who fell in love with his own reflection?

O Who was the first professional boxer to defeat Lennox Lewis?

P Little Marvels and Hurst Green Shafts are both types of what?

Q What name is given to an event that occurs once every five years?

R Who was hanged after being found guilty of murdering David Blakely?

S In which county is the resort of Minehead?

T How are the Cistercians of the Strict Observance more commonly known?

U Which element was named after a planet discovered in 1871?

V Which TV series featured a submarine called the *Seaview*?

W On June 7th 2000, members of which organisation made new headlines for heckling Tony Blair?

X How is forty written in Roman numerals?

Y Vince Clarke and Alison Moyet made up which pop duo?

Z Frank Beard was appropriately a member of which pop group?

ANSWERS
N. Narcissus O. Oliver McCall P. Peas Q. Quinquennial R. Ruth Ellis S. Somerset T. Trappist U. Uranium V. *Voyage To The Bottom Of The Sea* W. Women's Institute X. XL Y. Yazoo Z. ZZ Top

QUIZ TWO

A What opened its doors for the first time in 1979 and is situated 24 kilometres (15 miles) east of Stoke-on-Trent?

B What is the common name of a wood hyacinth?

C What name is given to the chief member of a lifeboat crew?

D What does a mysophobic person fear?

E What actor played Axel Foley in three films?

F Which TV family lived in Stone Cave Road and had a pet called Dino?

G What was the name of the car in *The Dukes of Hazzard*?

H What name is given to the rules that govern American football?

I What name is given to a manager of an opera or concert series?

J Which album by Alanis Morissette became the best ever selling album by a woman?

K What is the alternative name for a jack in a pack of cards?

L Which actor was painted with luminous green make-up when he played the Incredible Hulk?

M Who became the first female American Secretary of State?

QUIZ TWO

N What is the technical name for laughing gas?

O Who formed her own company called Harpo Productions?

P In which sitcom did Nicholas Lyndhurst play an unlikely spy?

Q What word is the name given to the minimum number of people required at a meeting to make the proceedings valid?

R Which Polish actress married and divorced Dennis Waterman?

S Which is the largest species of cat?

T Which Poet Laureate died in October 1998?

U Which pop group took their name from an unemployment benefit form?

V Trinidad lies off the coast of which country?

W What name is given to the seventh Sunday after Easter?

X Which group had a Top 10 disco hit in 1991 with a song called 'Move Your Body'?

Y YOP schemes were introduced by the Tory government to combat unemployment for school leavers. What did the initials YOP stand for?

Z What was the name of the saxophonist in the Muppets band?

ANSWERS

N. Nitrous Oxide O. Oprah Winfrey P. *Piglet files* Q. Quorum R. Rula Lenska S. Siberian Tiger T. Ted Hughes U. UB40 V. Venezuela W. Whitsun X. Xpansions Y. Youth Opportunities Programme Z. Zoot

QUIZ THREE

A What was the name of the diner frequented by the cast in the sitcom *Happy Days*?

B What is Foyles of London famous for selling?

C What was the surname of Buffalo Bill?

D In which city is Mahatma Ghandi Park?

E What was the maiden name of Linda McCartney?

F What six-letter word is the name given to a picture painted onto a wall?

G Kwame Nkrumah was the first ever president of which country?

H Who died in 1989 after 62 years in power?

I What name is given to a line on a map connecting places of equal temperature?

J Who was the head of the FBI for 48 years?

K What is the collective term for a group of toads?

L King Idris was the last reigning monarch of which African country?

M Who did John Prescott succeed as Deputy Leader of the Labour Party?

QUIZ THREE

N Who did Ewan McGregor play in the film *Rogue Trader*?

O What is the singular of Ova?

P In which film does the lead character say 'a boy's best friend is his mother'?

Q What name is given to the measure of 24 sheets of paper?

R Which TV comedy drama featured the antics of a taxi firm called Cresta Cabs?

S In which city is *The Full Monty* set?

T What is an alternative name for a bullfighter?

U What is the name of the trophy presented to the winner of the Women's World Championship in badminton?

V What is the stage name of the comedian Jim Moir?

W Which 1998 film told the story of a dead Irish lottery winner?

X What determines the female gender?

Y What does a red triangle signify on an ordnance survey map?

Z What is the alternative name for a courgette?

ANSWERS

N. Nick Leeson O. Ovum P. *Psycho* Q. Quire R. *Roger, Roger* S. Sheffield T. Toreador U. Uber Cup V. Vic Reeves W. *Waking Ned* X. X Chromosome Y. Youth Hostel Z. Zucchini

QUIZ FOUR

A How is Sacha Baron Cohen better known?

B From which city was the *Titanic* launched in 1912?

C Which composer's life story was told in the film *A Song To Remember*?

D Which team won the Superbowl in 1998?

E The leaves of which tree provide the staple diet of koala bears?

F What is the surname of the character played by Robbie Coltrane in *Cracker*?

G Which fabled beast had the head of an eagle and the body of a lion?

H Reputedly whose last words were 'let us now relieve the Romans of their fears by the death of a feeble old man'?

I Corfu and Zante are members of which Greek island group?

J Who did Priscilla Presley play in *Dallas*?

K Which actor starred in the films *Speed* and *The Matrix*?

L What is the alternative name for a peewit?

M Which American state was named after the wife of Charles I?

QUIZ FOUR

N On August 9th 1945 an atom bomb was dropped on which city?

O What was the title of the first solo UK No. I hit for Michael Jackson?

P What name is given to a square slab at the foot of a column?

Q What was the surname of the singer who topped the charts with 'Devilgate Drive'?

R What is the fortieth wedding anniversary?

S Who left Bananarama to marry Dave Stewart?

T What do Americans call a dinner jacket?

U Who was the last king of Italy?

V Which comic features the characters of Sid the Sexist and Finbarr Saunders?

W Which football club is nicknamed the Chairboys?

X What type of vision is possessed by Superman?

Y If all the No. I hits of the 20th century were listed alphabetically, which would come last?

Z Which *Magic Roundabout* character ended each episode with the words 'Time for bed'?

QUIZ FIVE

A Who was the Captain of the Pequod in *Moby-Dick*?

B Which Dickens novel is set during the Gordon riots?

C Who wrote the novel *Children of the New Forest*?

D Who rode a horse called Rosinante?

E What was the name of the donkey in the *Winnie the Pooh* books?

F Which feline character was created by Otto Mesmer?

G What was the sequel to *Gentlemen Prefer Blondes* written by Anita Loos?

H What sort of creature is Bilbo Baggins?

I Which literary hero falls in love with Rowena?

J Tom Cruise starred in the film *The Firm*. Who wrote the novel?

K Which adventure novel features a ship called *The Covenant*?

L What was the name of the land of the little people in *Gulliver's Travel*?

M Which Shakespeare play features the character of Constable Dogberry?

QUIZ FIVE

N What was the name of the dictatorial pig in *Animal Farm*?

O Which book by Charles Darwin chronicled his controversial theories on evolution?

P Who went around the world in eighty days?

Q What was the name of the hunchback created by Victor Hugo?

R Who was nicknamed the Bard of Ayrshire?

S What does the S stand for in the name T S Eliot?

T What is the name of Henry Williamson's literary otter?

U Which rock group took their name from a character in David Copperfield?

V Becky Sharp is the central character in which novel?

W Which epic novel by Tolstoy is set during the Napoleonic wars?

X Who wrote the book *The Happy Hooker*?

Y What is title of the autobiography penned by Sammy Davis Jnr?

Z How is Don Diego de la Vega better known?

ANSWERS

N. Napoleon O. *Origin of a Species* P. Phileas Fog Q. Quasimodo R. Robbie Burns
S. Stearns T. Tarka U. Uriah Heep V. *Vanity Fair* W. *War and Peace* X. Xaviera Hollander
Y. *Yes I Can* Z. Zorro